Rachel Cooper

SHOW MUSIC FOR SAXOPHONE

WISE PUBLICATIONS
LONDON/NEW YORK/SYDNEY

EXCLUSIVE DISTRIBUTORS:
MUSIC SALES LIMITED
8/9 FRITH STREET, LONDON W1V 5TZ, ENGLAND.
MUSIC SALES PTY LIMITED
120 ROTHSCHILD AVENUE, ROSEBERY, NSW 2018, AUSTRALIA.

ORDER NO.AM74030
ISBN 0.7119.1783.3

BOOK AND COVER DESIGN BY PEARCE MARCHBANK STUDIO
COVER PHOTOGRAPHY BY ROD SHONE
COMPILED BY PETER EVANS
ARRANGED BY ROBIN DE SMET
MUSIC PROCESSED BY MUSIC PRINT LIMITED
TYPESET BY THE PRINTED WORD LIMITED

PRINTED IN THE UNITED KINGDOM BY
J.B. OFFSET PRINTERS (MARKS TEY) LIMITED, MARKS TEY, ESSEX.

EDELWEISS

WORDS BY OSCAR HAMMERSTEIN II
MUSIC BY RICHARD RODGERS

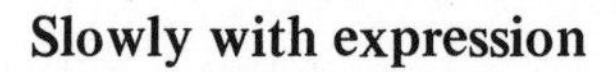

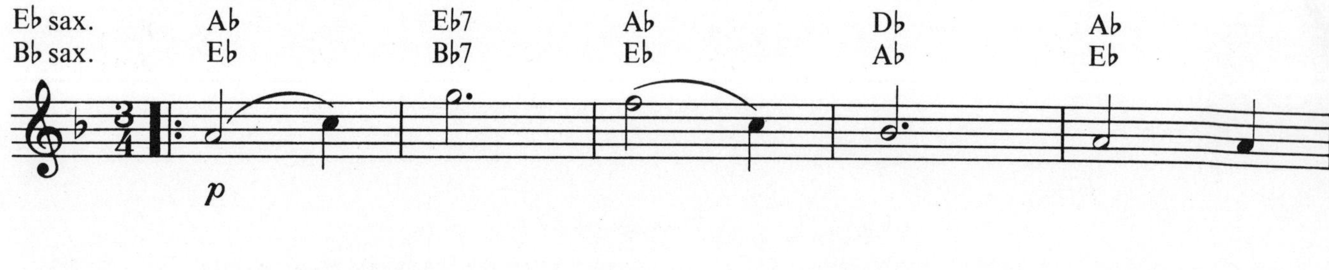

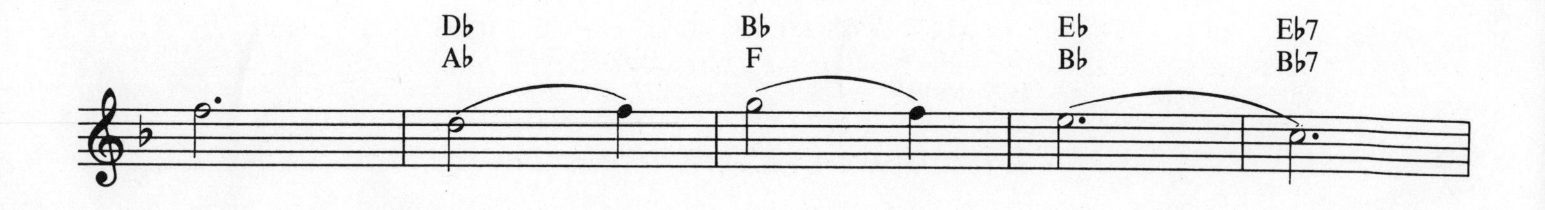

CLIMB EV'RY MOUNTAIN

WORDS BY OSCAR HAMMERSTEIN II
MUSIC BY RICHARD RODGERS

THIS NEARLY WAS MINE

WORDS BY OSCAR HAMMERSTEIN II
MUSIC BY RICHARD RODGERS

A WOMAN IN LOVE

WORDS & MUSIC BY FRANK LOESSER

YOUNGER THAN SPRINGTIME

WORDS BY OSCAR HAMMERSTEIN II
MUSIC BY RICHARD RODGERS

OH, WHAT A BEAUTIFUL MORNIN'

WORDS BY OSCAR HAMMERSTEIN II
MUSIC BY RICHARD RODGERS

Moderate waltz time

TONIGHT

MUSIC BY LEONARD BERNSTEIN
LYRICS BY STEPHEN SONDHEIM

DON'T CRY FOR ME ARGENTINA

MUSIC BY ANDREW LLOYD WEBBER
LYRICS BY TIM RICE

STRANGER IN PARADISE

WORDS & MUSIC BY ROBERT WRIGHT & GEORGE FORREST

D7 Am7 D7 Gmaj7 G6
A7 Em7 A7 Dmaj7 D6
Cm7 F7 B♭maj7
Gm7 C7 Fmaj7
Bdim Cm7 F7
F♯dim Gm7 C7
B♭maj7 B♭6 E♭ Cm7
Fmaj7 F6 B♭ Gm7
E♭m7 F7 B♭6 Dm Gm7
B♭m7 C7 F6 Am Dm7
3
C7 F9 Dm B♭
G7 C9 Am F
G7 Bdim Cm7 E♭m F7
D7 F♯dim Gm7 B♭m C7
B♭ A♭9 G♭6 B♭
F E♭9 D♭6 F
poco rit.
p

TILL THERE WAS YOU

WORDS & MUSIC BY MEREDITH WILLSON

PEOPLE WILL SAY WE'RE IN LOVE

WORDS BY OSCAR HAMMERSTEIN II
MUSIC BY RICHARD RODGERS

BALI HA'I

WORDS BY OSCAR HAMMERSTEIN II
MUSIC BY RICHARD RODGERS

B♭dim
Fdim
B♭
F
A
E
G♭7
D♭7
B♭
F
G♭7
D♭7
F7
C7
B♭7
F7
E♭
B♭
F9
C9
1.
B♭6
F6
Adim
Edim
Gm
Dm
mf
Adim
Edim
Gm
Dm
Cdim
Gdim
B♭6
F6
Cdim
Gdim
Gm
Dm
Cdim
Gdim
Gm
Dm
C♭
G♭
D♭
A♭
E♭
B♭
D♭
A♭
E♭
B♭
G♭
D♭
A♭
E♭
B♭
F
Fmaj7
Cmaj7
2.
B♭6
F6

AIN'T MISBEHAVIN'

WORDS BY ANDY RAZAF
MUSIC BY THOMAS WALLER & HARRY BROOKS

Bb9
F9
Eb7+5
Bb7+5
Fm
Cm
f
Db7
Ab7
Bb7
F7
F7
C7
Eb
Bb
Edim
Bdim
Fm
Cm
Fm7
Cm7
Bb7
F7
Eb7
Bb7
F7
C7
Bb7
F7
Eb7
Bb7
Ab
Eb
Adim
Edim
mf
Bbm7
Fm7
Eb7
Bb7
Ab
Eb
C7+5
G7+5
Db6
Ab6
Gb9
Db9
Ab
Eb
Cb7
Gb7
Bbm7
Fm7
Eb7
Bb7
1.
C7+5
G7+5
F7
C7
Bb7
F7
Eb7
Bb7
2.
Ab
Eb
Db7
Ab7
Ab
Eb

THE MUSIC OF THE NIGHT

MUSIC BY ANDREW LLOYD WEBBER
LYRICS BY CHARLES HART
ADDITIONAL LYRIC BY RICHARD STILGOE

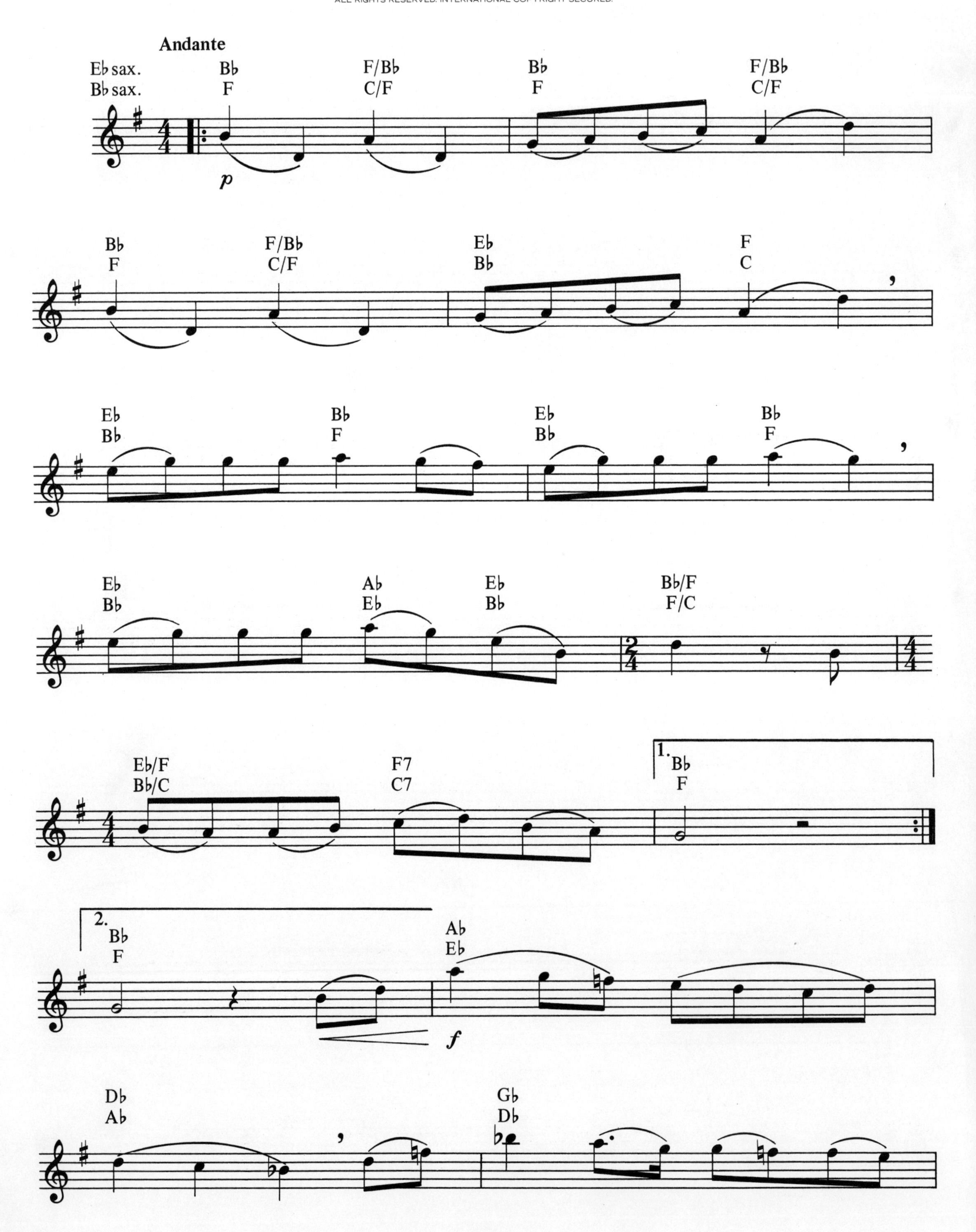

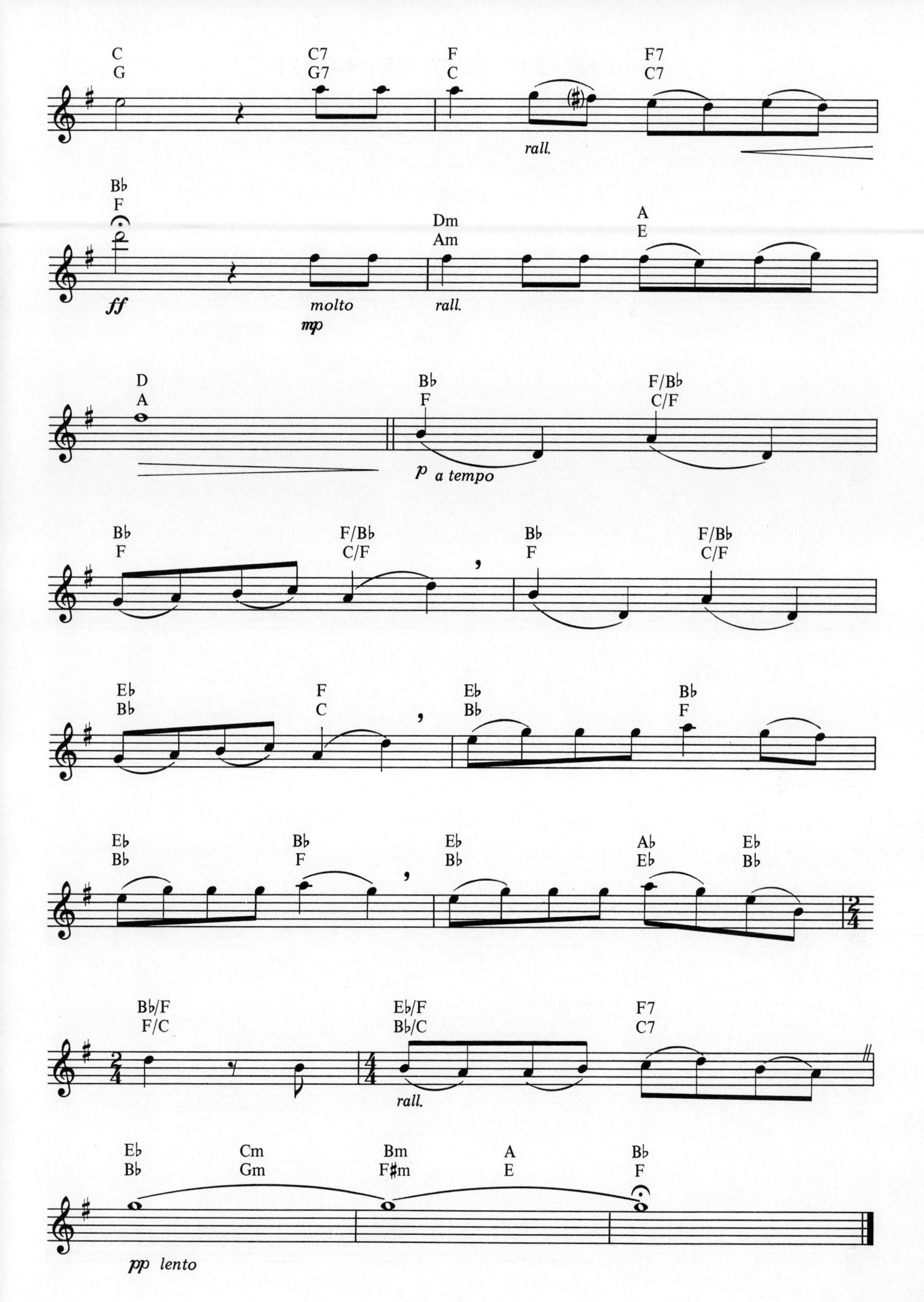
C
G
C7
G7
F
C
F7
C7
rall.
B♭
F
ff
molto
mp
Dm
Am
rall.
A
E
D
A
B♭
F
p a tempo
F/B♭
C/F
B♭
F
F/B♭
C/F
B♭
F
F/B♭
C/F
E♭
B♭
F
C
E♭
B♭
B♭
F
E♭
B♭
B♭
F
E♭
B♭
A♭
E♭
E♭
B♭
B♭/F
F/C
E♭/F
B♭/C
rall.
F7
C7
E♭
B♭
Cm
Gm
Bm
F♯m
A
E
B♭
F
pp lento

WONDERFUL COPENHAGEN

WORDS & MUSIC BY FRANK LOESSER

DIAMONDS ARE A GIRL'S BEST FRIEND

WORDS BY LEO ROBIN
MUSIC BY JULE STYNE

CABARET

MUSIC BY JOHN KANDER
LYRICS BY FRED EBB

MEMORY

MUSIC BY ANDREW LLOYD WEBBER
TEXT BY TREVOR NUNN AFTER T.S. ELIOT

I DON'T KNOW HOW TO LOVE HIM

MUSIC BY ANDREW LLOYD WEBBER
LYRICS BY TIM RICE

TELL ME ON A SUNDAY

WORDS BY DON BLACK
MUSIC BY ANDREW LLOYD WEBBER

AS TIME GOES BY

WORDS & MUSIC BY HERMAN HUPFELD

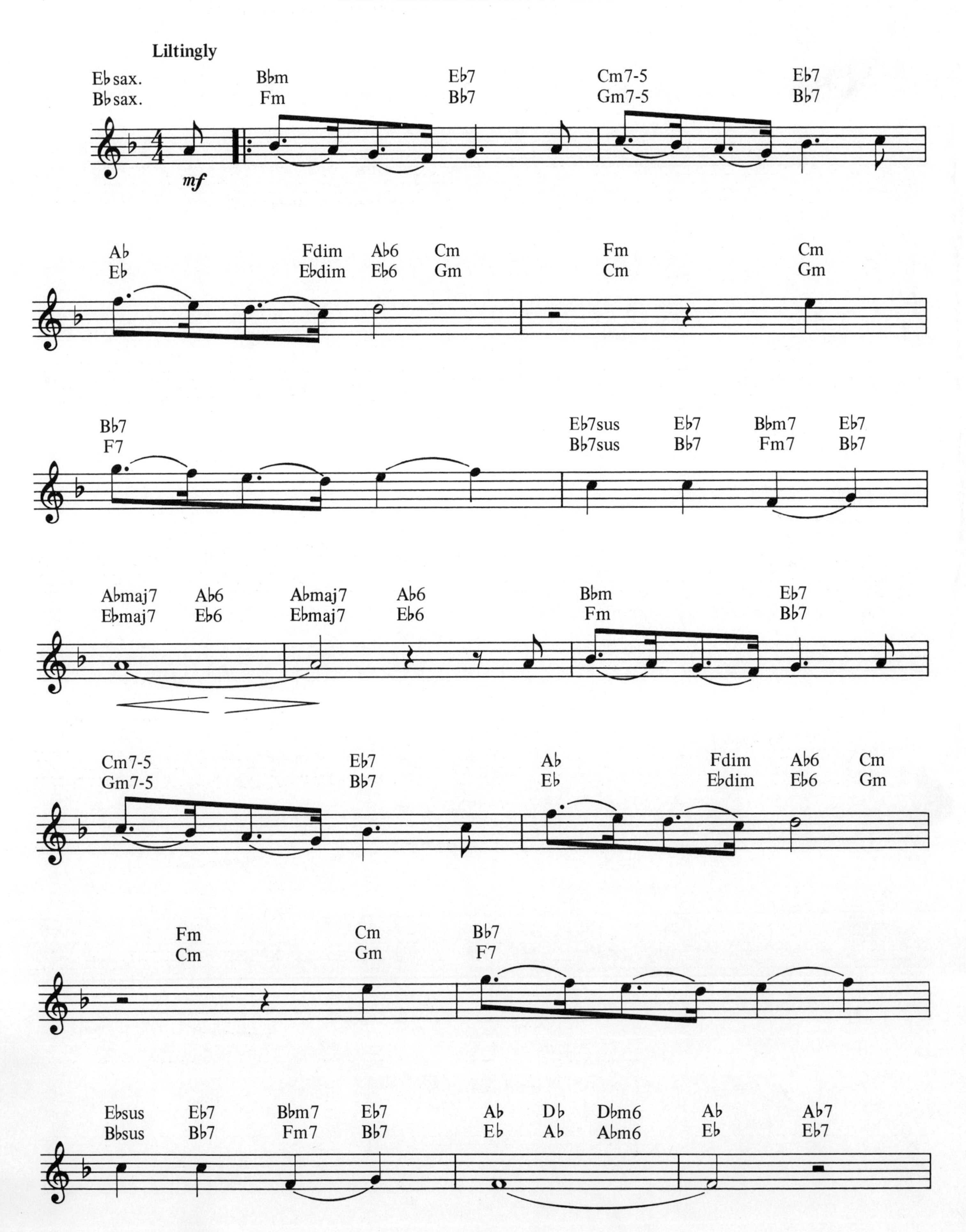

D♭
A♭
F7
C7
poco a poco cresc.

B♭m
Fm
Bdim
F♯dim
Fm
Cm
D♭7
A♭7
B♭9
F9
E♭9
B♭9
E♭dim
B♭dim
E♭7
B♭7
B♭m
Fm
E♭7
B♭7
poco rit.
mf a tempo
Cm7-5
Gm7-5
E♭7
B♭7
A♭
E♭
Fdim
E♭dim
A♭6
E♭6
Cm
Gm
Fm
Cm
Cm
Gm
B♭7
F7
E♭6
B♭6
A♭
E♭
Cm
Gm
Adim
Edim
B♭m7
Fm7
E♭7
B♭7
E♭7+
B♭7+
1.
A♭
E♭
Fm
Cm
B♭9
F9
E♭7
B♭7
2.
A♭
E♭
G♭9
D♭9
A♭
E♭

I FEEL PRETTY

MUSIC BY LEONARD BERNSTEIN
LYRICS BY STEPHEN SONDHEIM

Ab Eb7 Ab Eb7
Eb Bb7 Eb Bb7
p
Ab Fm Eb
Eb Cm Bb
Eb7 D7 Gm Ebm
Bb7 A7 Dm Bbm
cresc.
Bb7 Fm7 Bb7 Bb+ Eb
F7 Cm7 F7 F+ Bb
f
p
Bb+ Eb Bb+ Eb Bb+ Eb
F+ Bb F+ Bb F+ Bb
Fm7 Bb Fm7 Bb7 Cm Cm7
Cm7 F Cm7 F7 Gm Gm7
f
Fm7 Bb7 Eb Db Bb
Cm7 F7 Bb Ab F
1. Eb Bb+
Bb F+
p
2. Eb
Bb

THE UGLY DUCKLING

WORDS & MUSIC BY FRANK LOESSER

Eb Ab Eb Fm Eb Bb7 Eb
Bb Eb Bb Cm Bb F7 Bb
Ab Eb Fm Eb Bb7 Eb Bb
Eb Bb Cm Bb F7 Bb F
legato
Ab Bb Ab Bb Ab
Eb F Eb F Eb
Bb F7 Bb F7+ Bb Ab Bb Ab Bb Ab
F C7 F C7+ F Eb F Eb F Eb
3
f
Bb F7 Bb Bb7-9 Abm6
F C7 F F7-9 Ebm6
D.%. al Coda
CODA
Bb Fm7 Bb Ab Eb F Bb
F Cm7 F Eb Bb C F
Eb Edim A7 Fm Bb7-5 Ab Bb7 Eb Fm7
Bb Bdim E7 Cm F7-5 Eb F7 Bb Cm7
Ab Eb Fm7 Eb Bb7 Eb
Eb Bb Cm7 Bb F7 Bb

ALL I ASK OF YOU

MUSIC BY ANDREW LLOYD WEBBER
LYRICS BY CHARLES HART

Bb F Gm7 Dm7 Cm7 Gm7 F C Bb/D F/A Gm7 Dm7 Cm7 Gm7 F C F6 C6 F7 C7
f
Bb F Gm7 Dm7 Cm7 Gm7 F C Bb/D F/A Eb Bb
Bb/F F/C Cm7/F Gm7/C F6 C6 Cm7/F Gm7/C Bb F Gm7 Dm7 Cm7 Gm7 F C
rit.
molto rit.
f
a tempo
Bb/D F/A Gm7 Dm7 Cm7 Gm7 Cm7/F Gm7/C Bb F Gm7 Dm7
Cm7 Gm7 F C Bb/D F/A Eb Bb Bb/F F/C Cm7/F Gm7/C F6 C6 Cm7/F Gm7/C
rit.
molto rit.
Bb F Gm7 Dm7 Bb F Gm7 Dm7 Cm7 Gm7 F C Bb/D F/A Gm7 Dm7
f a tempo
Cm7 Gm7 Cm7/F Gm7/C Bb F Gm7 Dm7 Cm7 Gm7 F C
f
C/D G/A Eb Bb Bb/F F/C Cm7/F Gm7/C F6 C6 Cm7/F Gm7/C Bb F
ff largo
mp
molto rit.

SEND IN THE CLOWNS

WORDS & MUSIC BY STEPHEN SONDHEIM

Bbm
Fm
Ebm7
Bbm7
Bb
F
Gb6/Db
Db6/Ab
Ab7/C
Eb7/G
Cb6
Gb6
Bbsus
Fsus
Abm7-5
Ebm7-5
Bbm/Db
Fm/Ab
Cb6/Db
Gb6/Ab
Db/Gb
Ab/Db
Cb
Gb
Db/Gb
Ab/Db
Cb
Gb
poco rit.
Gb
Db
Gbsus
Dbsus
Gb
Db
Gbmaj9
Dbmaj9
a tempo
Gb
Db
Cbmaj9
Gbmaj9
Cb6
Gb6
Db7/Gb
Ab7/Db
1.
Db9/Gb
Ab9/Db
Gb
Db
Gbsus
Dbsus
Gb
Db
Gbsus
Dbsus
2.
Db9/Gb
Ab9/Db
Gb
Db
Gbsus
Dbsus
Gb
Db
poco rit.
a tempo

SOMEWHERE

MUSIC BY LEONARD BERNSTEIN
LYRICS BY STEPHEN SONDHEIM

MARIA

MUSIC BY LEONARD BERNSTEIN
LYRICS BY STEPHEN SONDHEIM

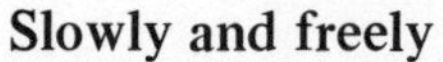

AMERICA

MUSIC BY LEONARD BERNSTEIN
LYRICS BY STEPHEN SONDHEIM

ANOTHER SUITCASE IN ANOTHER HALL

MUSIC BY ANDREW LLOYD WEBBER
LYRICS BY TIM RICE

BIG SPENDER

WORDS BY DOROTHY FIELDS
MUSIC BY CY COLEMAN

G7
D7
Cm
Gm
mf
(Tacet)
3
C
G
Em
Bm
Am
Em
C
G
Dm
Am
A+
E+
Dm7
Am7
Ab9
Eb9
G9
D9
Ab9
Eb9
G9
D9
D.S. al Coda
3
mp
CODA
Db
Ab
f
Cm
Gm
Ab9
Eb9
mf
G9
D9
Cm
Gm
Ab7
Eb7
mp
Cm
Gm
Ab7
Eb7
p
Cm
Gm
f

I DREAMED A DREAM

MUSIC BY CLAUDE-MICHEL SCHONBERG
LYRICS BY HERBERT KRETZMER
ORIGINAL TEXT BY ALAIN BOUBLIL & JEAN-MARC NATEL

Ab Eb
Ab/G Eb/D
Fm7 Cm7
Ab/Eb Eb/Bb
Dbmaj7 Abmaj7
Eb11 Bb11
Ab Eb
Eb/G Bb/D
Ebm6/Gb Bbm6/Db
F7sus C7sus
F7 C7
Bb F
Bb/A F/E
Gm Dm
Bb/F F/C
f
Eb Bb
Eb/D Bb/A
Cm7 Gm7
F13 C13
F7 C7
Bb F
Bb/A F/E
Gm7 Dm7
Bb/F F/C
Ebmaj7 Bbmaj7
Ebmaj7/D Bbmaj7/A
Cm7 Gm7
F13 C13
F7 C7
Bb F
Bb/A F/E
Gm Dm
Bb/F F/C
Eb Bb
Bb/D F/A
3
3
Cm7 Gm7
Eb11 Bb11
F C
Bb F
Bb/A F/E
Gm7 Dm7
Bb/F F/C
Eb Bb
F7 C7
Bb F
Bb/A F/E
mf
p
Gm7 Dm7
Bb/D F/A
Eb Bb
F7 C7
Bb F
rit.
pp

SUPERSTAR

MUSIC BY ANDREW LLOYD WEBBER
LYRICS BY TIM RICE

B♭7
F7
F7
C7
F
C
B♭
F
E♭
B♭
B♭
F
F
C
F
C
B♭
F
E♭
B♭
B♭
F
F
C
B♭
F
E♭
B♭
B♭
F
1.
F
C
A♭
E♭
B♭
F
Bdim
F♯dim
F
C
A♭
E♭
B♭
F
Bdim
F♯dim
F
C
A♭
E♭
B♭
F
Bdim
F♯dim
F
C
Tacet - - - - - - -
(D.C.)
2.
F
C
F
C
B♭
F
E♭
B♭
B♭
F
F
C